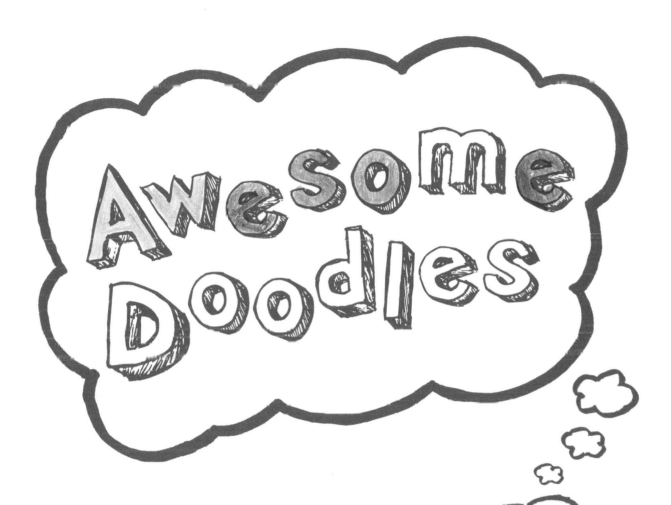

Awesome Doodles

SCHOLASTIC

New York • Toronto • London • Auckland
Sydney • Mexico City • New Delhi • Hong Kong

Doodles by
Kirsteen Harris-Jones

ISBN 978-0-545-22940-1

10 9 8 7 6 5 4 3 2   11 12 13 14

Printed in the U.S.A.   08
First Scholastic edition, January 2010

What's hatching?

Superhero!

Give this boy a mouth full of braces.

What's out there?

Butterflies or flowers?

Up, up, and away . . .
Finish the hot-air balloons.

Make a big splash!

Paint a picture of yourself.

Strange pet!

What's cooking on the barbecue?

Give the dinosaurs spikes and scales.

How does your garden grow?

. . . and the giant tumbled
from the beanstalk.

Finish the X-ray.

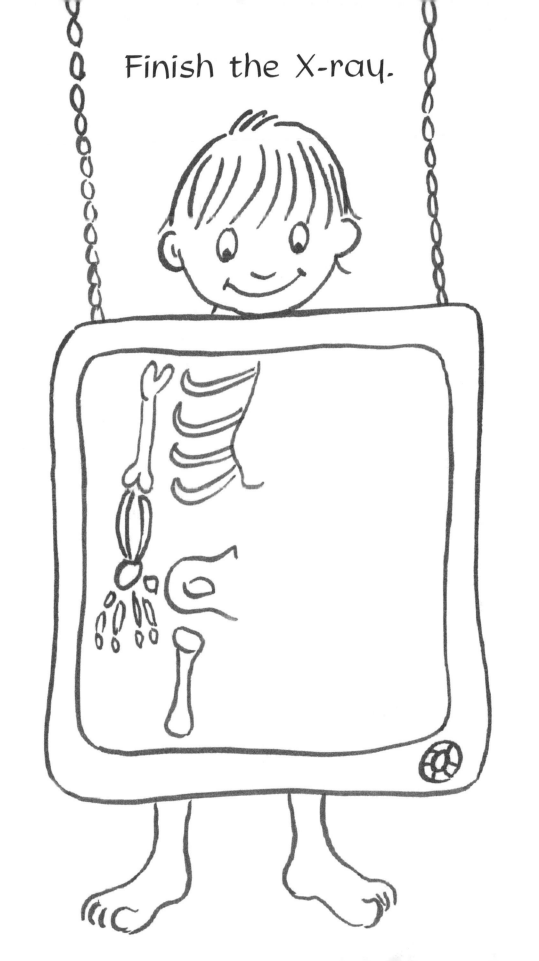

Fill the reef with sea creatures.

Who's playing under the tree?

What's inside the backpack?

Gulp . . . Whose shadow is that?

What has escaped from the cage?

Lions or tigers?

Draw him a twin.

WATER FIGHT!

Give the cowboy a hat.

What is hiding in the jungle?

That shouldn't be in there!

What did the snake swallow?

What did the boy swallow?

Draw the alien visitor.

What did she drop?

Give all the animals ears.

What's so funny?

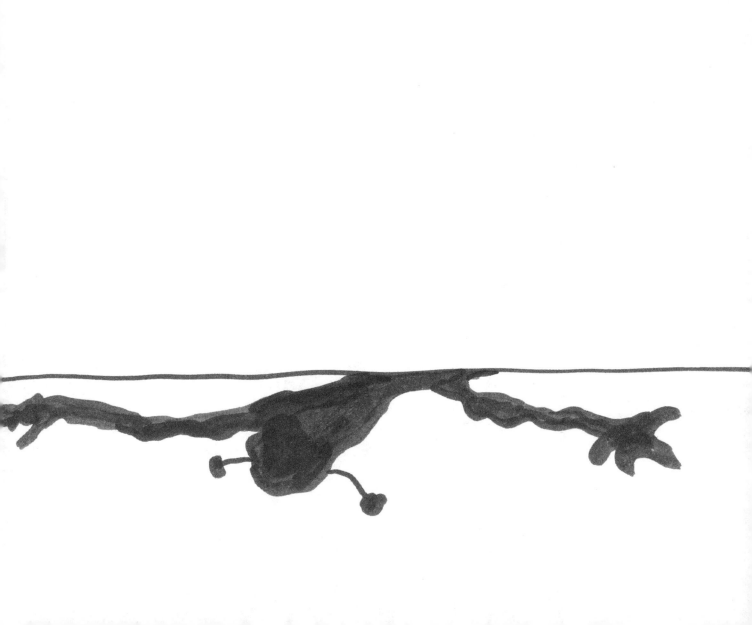

The world's wriggliest worm.

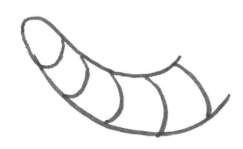

Where did he bury his bone?

A lot of bubbles!

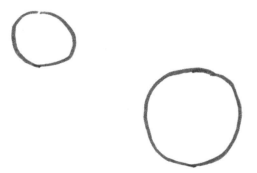

Happy or sad?

Design the perfect car for a clown.

Crown them King . . .

. . . and Queen.

Build a blazing campfire.

Give the ballplayer a cap.

What made the baby yell?

Give all the animals tails.

Parachutes or umbrellas?

What can the astronaut see?

Build the town's tallest tower.

Quick! Get a ladder!

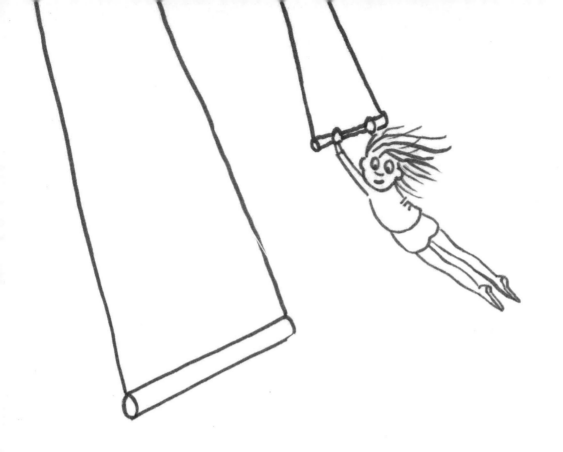

The Tremendous Trapeze Twins.

Fill the branches with birds.

Breakfast in bed.

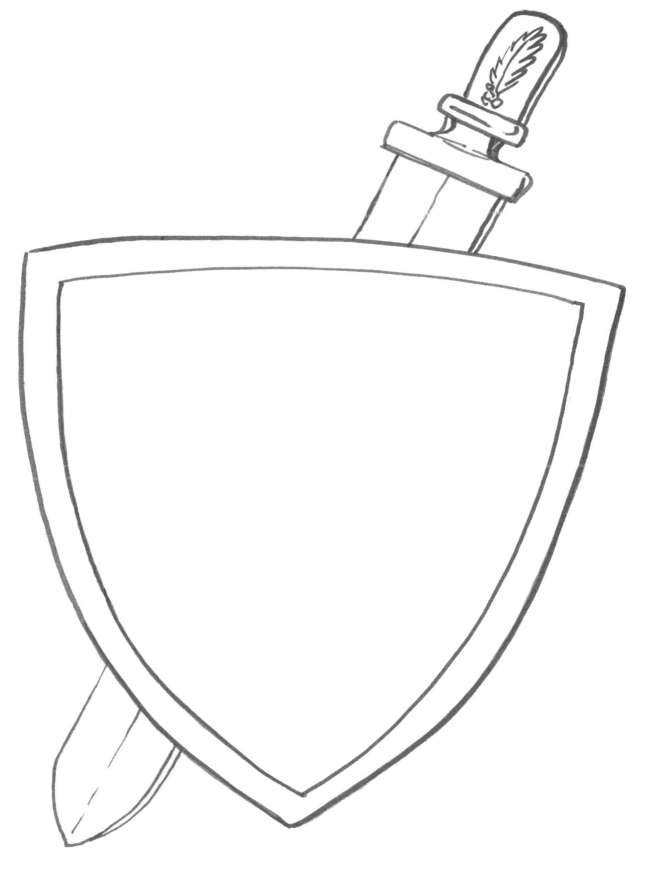

Design your own coat of arms.

Who is attacking the castle?

Draw the bird that did this.

Scary spider!

The world's best snowman.

What is he daydreaming
about in class?

What can he see on the water?

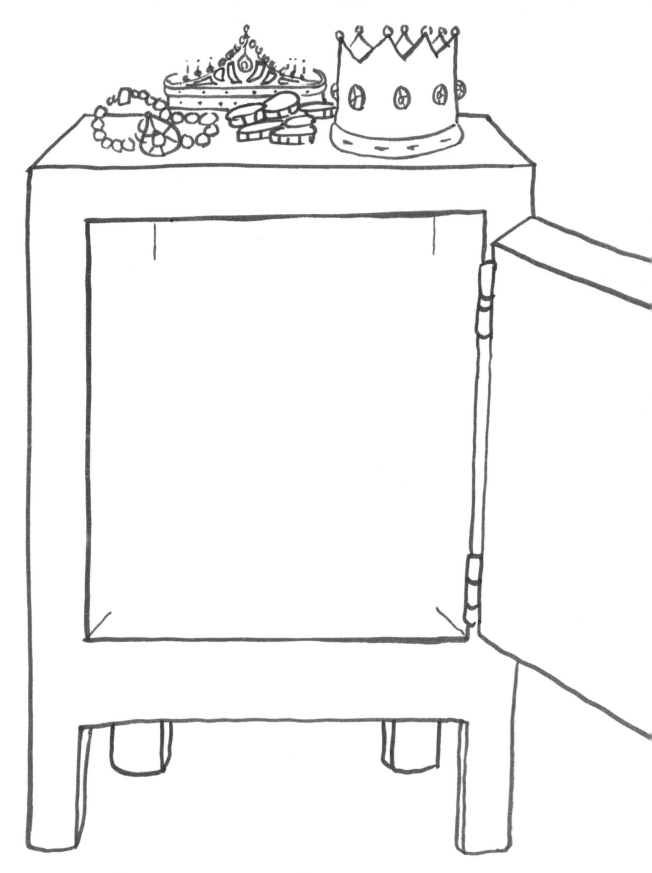

Fill the safe with treasures.

Killer breath!

Who is sneaking into the gopher's tunnel?

Complete the human pyramid.

Give him lots of vines to swing from.

Clocks or wheels?

What did he let out of the box?

Complete the totem poles.

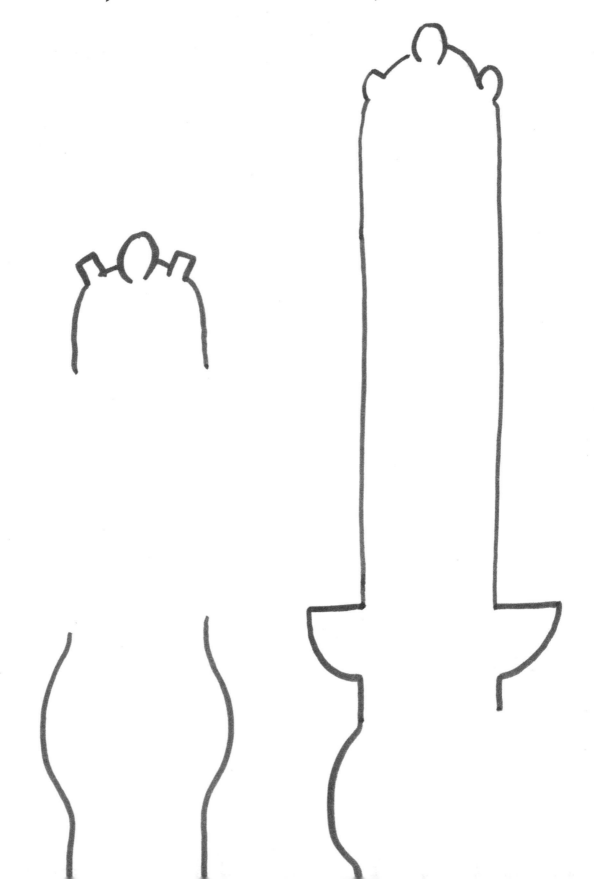

Land ahoy!

Fill the sky with fireworks.

What frightened the fish?

Draw the goblin some pets.

Yum!

What is hidden in the pharaoh's pyramid?

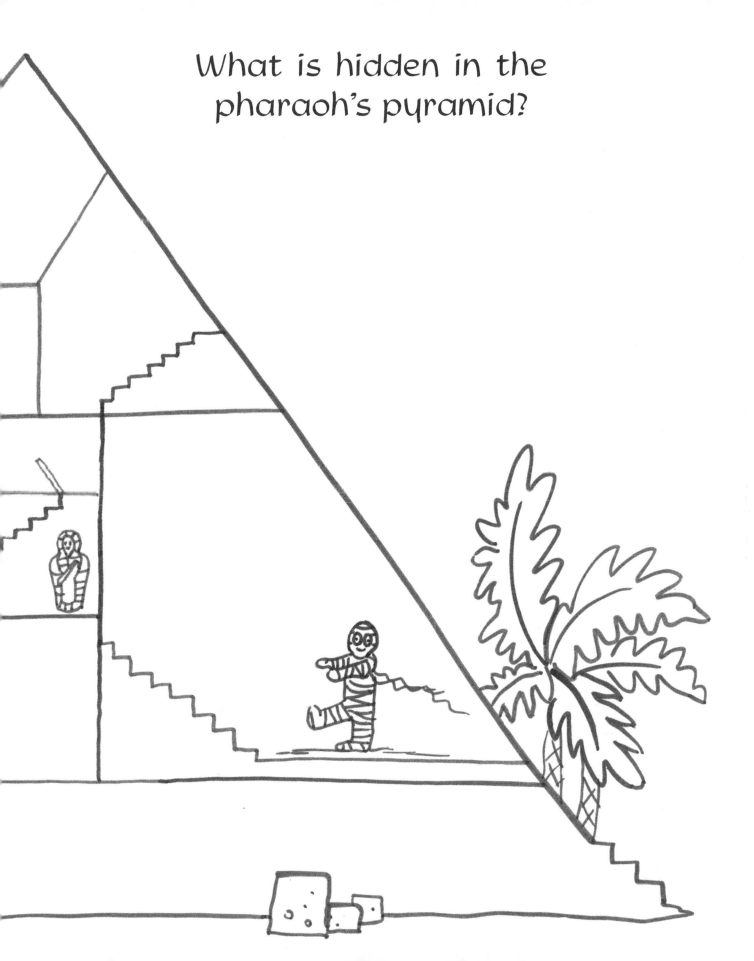

Who is he running from?

Finish the dinosaur.

Give the knight a helmet.

What made that noise?

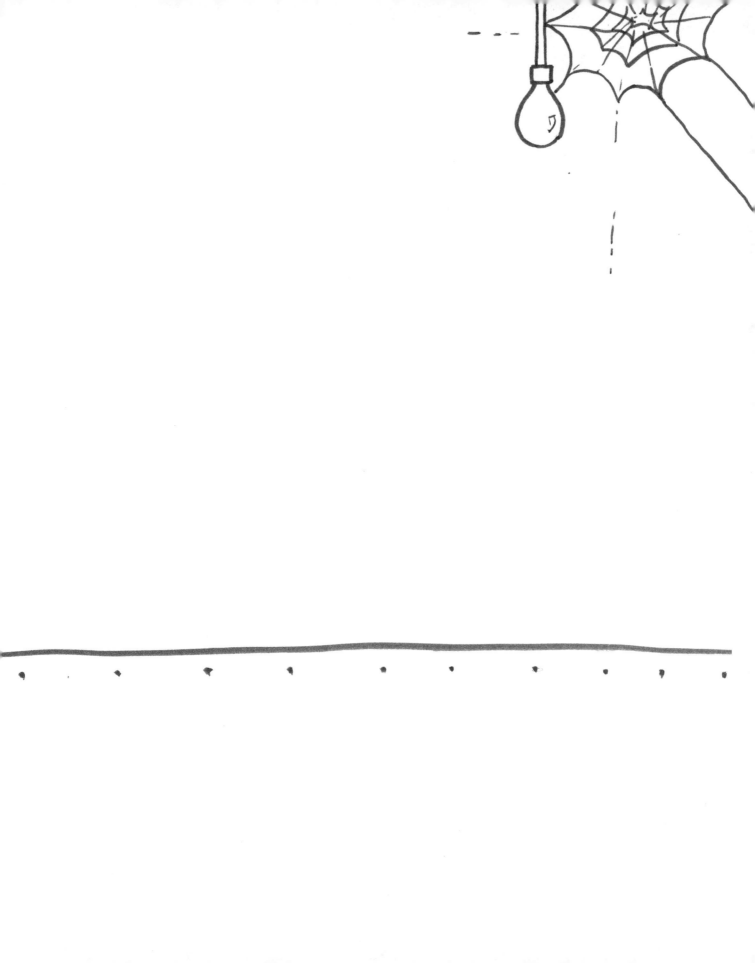

Fill the squirrel's hole with acorns and nuts.

Draw the waterfall.

Fill the night sky with shooting stars.

My prizewinning pet.

Where have you been on vacation?

Having a great time!

Great pizza.

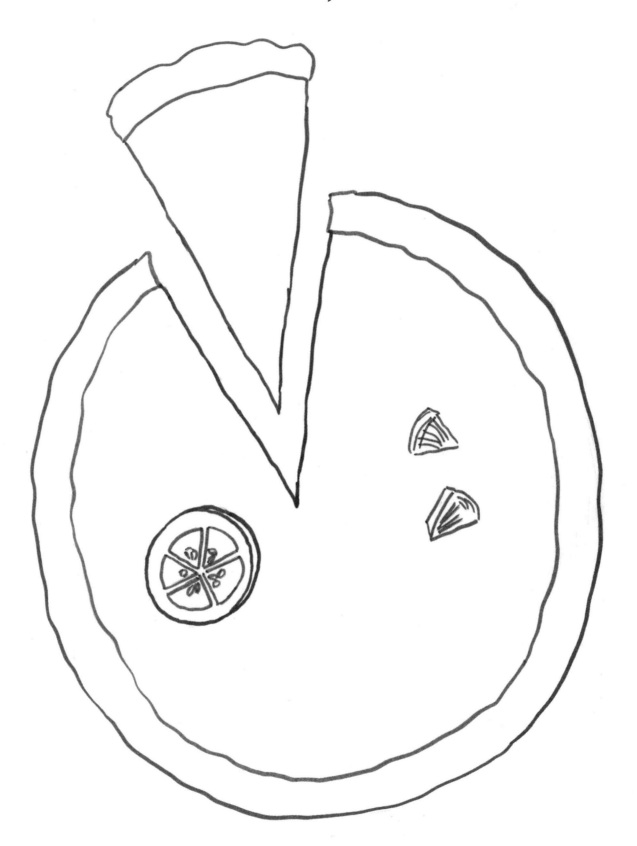

Gross pizza.

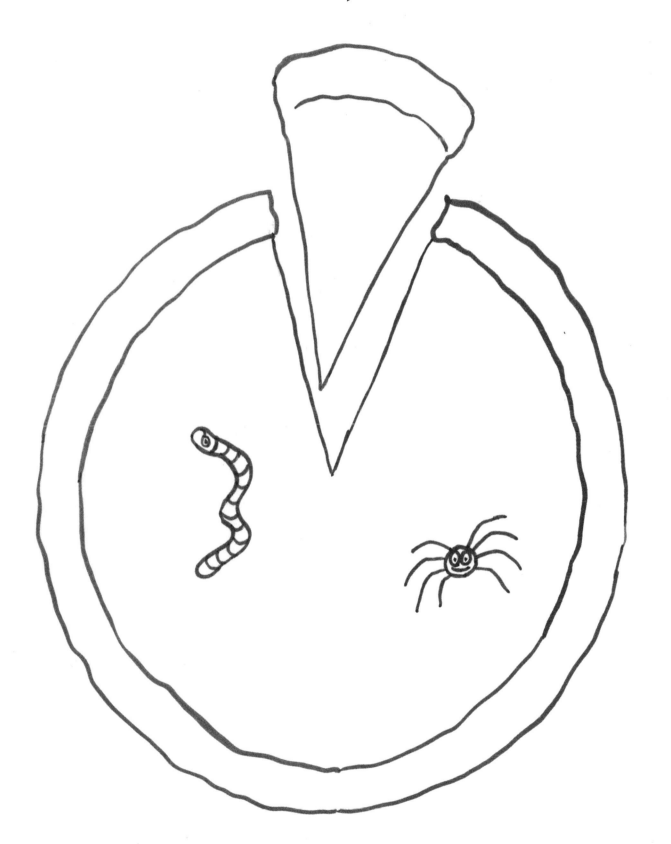

Add a haunted house
on the hill.

Look!

Snakes or snails?

Decorate the cake.

Scary!

Is there life on Mars?

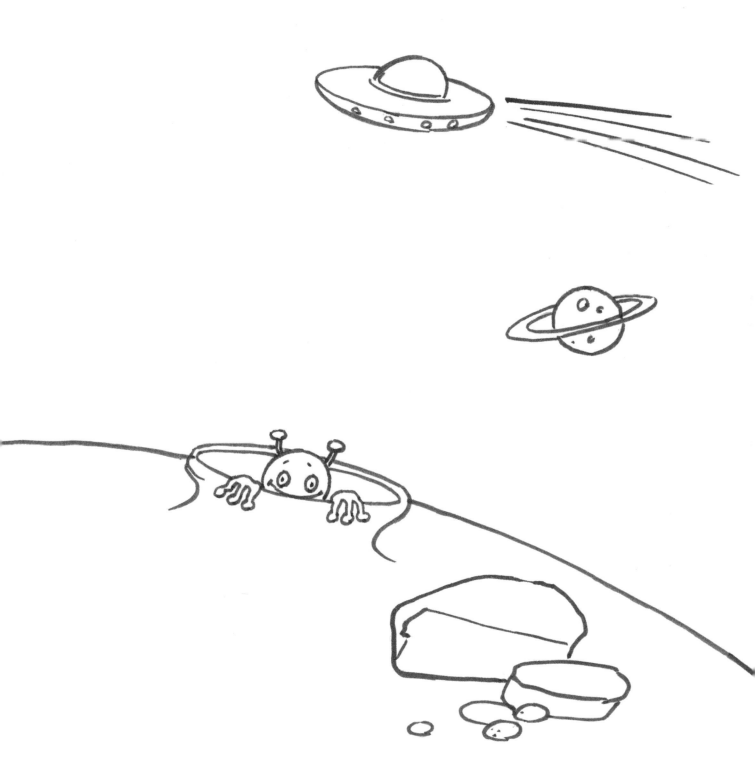

Decorate the wall.

Surf's up! Draw him a huge wave to ride.

What does she have on her head?

What is the lion scared of?

Heavy.

Light.

Oops, too many balloons.